Final accounts for sole traders and partnerships

Workbook

David Cox

Published by Osborne Books Limited
Unit 1B Everoak Estate
Bromyard Road, Worcester WR2 5HP
Tel 01905 748071
Email books@osbornebooks.co.uk
Website www.osbornebooks.co.uk

Design by Laura Ingham

Printed by CPI Group (UK) Limited, Croydon, CR0 4YY, on environmentally friendly, acid-free paper from managed forests.

British Library Cataloguing in Publication Data
A catalogue record for this book is available from the British Library

ISBN 978 1909173 170

Contents

Introduction

Chapter activities

Chapter activities – answers

Practice assessments – tasks

Practice assessments – answers

Acknowledgements

The publisher wishes to thank the following for their help with the reading and production of the book: Jean Cox, Jon Moore and Cathy Turner. Thanks are also due to Debbie Board for her technical editorial work and to Laura Ingham for her designs for this series.

The publisher is indebted to the Association of Accounting Technicians for its help and advice to our authors and editors during the preparation of this text.

Author

David Cox has more than twenty years' experience teaching accountancy students over a wide range of levels. Formerly with the Management and Professional Studies Department at Worcester College of Technology, he now lectures on a freelance basis and carries out educational consultancy work in accountancy studies. He is author and joint author of a number of textbooks in the areas of accounting, finance and banking.

Introduction

what this book covers

This book has been written to cover the 'Prepare final accounts for sole traders and partnerships' Unit which is mandatory for the revised (2013) AAT Level 3 Diploma in Accounting.

what this book contains

This book is set out in two sections:

- **Chapter Activities** which provide extra practice material in addition to the activities included in the Osborne Books Tutorial text. Answers to the Chapter activities are included in this book.

- **Practice Assessments** are provided to prepare the student for the Computer Based Assessments. They are based directly on the structure, style and content of the sample assessment material provided by the AAT at www.aat.org.uk. Suggested answers to the Practice Assessments are set out in this book.

further information

If you want to know more about our products and resources, please visit www.osbornebooks.co.uk for further details and access to our online shop.

Chapter activities

1 Preparing financial statements

1.1 Cost of sales is calcuated as:

	✔
Opening inventory + purchases – closing inventory	
Purchases – opening inventory + closing inventory	
Opening inventory + purchases + closing inventory	
Purchases – opening inventory – closing inventory	

1.2 Which **ONE** of the following is used to calculate profit for the year?

	✔
Two-column trial balance	
Sales ledger	
Statement of financial position	
Statement of profit or loss	

1.3 Which **ONE** of the following describes net current assets?

	✔
The excess of non-current assets over non-current liabilities	
The excess of current assets over non-current liabilities	
The excess of current assets over current liabilities	
The excess of non-current assets over current liabilities	

1.4   **You are to** fill in the missing figures for the following sole trader businesses:

	Sales	Opening inventory	Purchases	Closing inventory	Gross profit	Expenses	Profit/loss* for year
	£	£	£	£	£	£	£
Business A	20,000	5,000	10,000	3,000	....	4,000	....
Business B	35,000	8,000	15,000	5,000	....	....	10,000
Business C	....	6,500	18,750	7,250	18,500	11,750	....
Business D	45,250	9,500	....	10,500	20,750	....	10,950
Business E	71,250	....	49,250	9,100	22,750	24,450	....
Business F	25,650	4,950	13,750	....	11,550	....	−3,450

*   **Note**: a loss is indicated by a minus sign.

1.5   This Activity is about calculating missing balances and the accounting equation.

You are given the following information about a sole trader as at 1 April 20-4:

The value of assets and liabilities was:

•	Non-current assets at carrying amount	£35,400
•	Inventory	£12,200
•	Trade receivables	£21,650
•	Bank (overdrawn)	£3,240
•	Trade payables	£12,790

There were no other assets or liabilities.

(a)   Calculate the capital account balance as at 1 April 20-4.

£

(b)   On 30 April 20-4, a new machine is purchased for use in the business and is paid for immediately by bank payment. Tick the boxes to show what effect this transaction will have on the balances. You must choose **ONE** answer for **EACH** line.

✔

	Debit	Credit	No change
Non-current assets			
Trade receivables			
Trade payables			
Bank			
Capital			

(c)   Which of the following is best described as a non-current liability? Tick **ONE** answer.

✔

A bank loan repayable in two years' time	
A bank overdraft	
Trade payables	
Trade receivables	

1.6 The following trial balance has been extracted by Matt Smith at 31 December 20-4:

	Dr	Cr
	£	£
Opening inventory	14,350	
Purchases	114,472	
Sales revenue		259,688
Rent and rates	13,718	
Heating and lighting	12,540	
Payroll expenses	42,614	
Vehicle expenses	5,817	
Advertising	6,341	
Premises at cost	75,000	
Office equipment at cost	33,000	
Vehicles at cost	21,500	
Sales ledger control	23,854	
Bank	1,235	
Cash	125	
Capital		62,500
Drawings	12,358	
Loan from bank		35,000
Purchases ledger control		14,258
Value Added Tax		5,478
Closing inventory: statement of profit or loss		16,280
Closing inventory: statement of financial position	16,280	
	393,204	393,204

You are to prepare the financial statements of Matt Smith for the year ended 31 December 20-4, using the conventional format.

1.7 An extract from the trial balance of Lisa James is as follows:

Trial balance (extract) as at 31 March 20-7		
	Dr	Cr
	£	£
Opening inventory	17,540	
Sales revenue		127,500
Purchases	77,200	
Sales returns	2,150	
Purchases returns		3,040
Carriage in	680	
Carriage out	1,540	
Discount received		230
Discount allowed	470	
Other expenses	35,830	
Closing inventory: statement of profit or loss		19,960

You are to prepare the statement of profit or loss of Lisa James for the year ended 31 March 20-7, using the conventional format.

2   Incomplete records accounting

2.1 • Cost of sales for the year is £250,000.

  • Mark-up is 50%.

What is sales revenue for the year?

	✔
£375,000	
£125,000	
£250,000	
£500,000	

2.2 • Sales for the year are £200,000.

  • Margin is 30%.

  • Opening inventory is £15,000; closing inventory is £20,000.

What are purchases for the year?

	✔
£260,000	
£160,000	
£140,000	
£145,000	

2.3 You are preparing accounts from incomplete records. Trade payables at the start of the year were £16,400. During the year purchases on credit total £73,400, bank payments to trade payables total £68,100, purchases returns total £1,800, and discounts received total £400.

What is the trade payables figure at the end of the year?

	✔
£13,300	
£20,300	
£19,500	
£23,900	

2.4   Talib Zabbar owns a shop selling children's clothes. He is convinced that one of his employees is stealing goods from the shop. He asks you to calculate from the accounting records the value of inventory stolen. The following information is available for the year ended 31 March 20-2:

- sales for the year, £160,000

- opening inventory at the beginning of the year, £30,500

- purchases for the year, £89,500

- closing inventory at the end of the year, £21,500

- the gross sales margin achieved on all sales is 40 per cent

You are to calculate the value of inventory stolen (if any) during the year ended 31 March 20-2.

2.5 This Activity is about finding missing figures in ledger accounts where the records are incomplete.

You are working on the financial statements of a business for the year ended 31 March 20-8. You have the following information.

Day book summaries for the year	Net £	VAT £	Total £
Sales	102,000	20,400	122,400
Purchases	64,000	12,800	76,800
Sales returns	1,800	360	2,160
Purchases returns	1,240	248	1,488

All sales and purchases are on credit terms

Balances as at:	31 March 20-7 £	31 March 20-8 £
Trade receivables	16,250	18,110
Trade payables	10,380	not known

Further information:	Net £	VAT £	Total £
Administration expenses	22,000	4,400	26,400

Administration expenses are not included in the purchases figure in purchases day book

Bank summary	Dr £		Cr £
Balance b/d	10,680	Travel expenses	5,290
Sales ledger control	117,950	Administration expenses	26,400
Balance c/d	6,313	Purchases ledger control	72,833
		HMRC for VAT	2,760
		Drawings	10,500
		Payroll expenses	17,160
	134,943		134,943

There were no settlement (cash) discounts on payments made to trade payables.

(a)   Using the figures given on the previous page, prepare the sales ledger control account for the year ended 31 March 20-8. Show clearly settlement (cash) discounts as the balancing figure.

Sales ledger control account

(b)   Using the figures given on the previous page, prepare the purchases ledger control account for the year ended 31 March 20-8. Show clearly the trade payables figure at the end of the year as the balancing figure.

Purchases ledger control account

(c)   Find the closing balance for VAT by preparing the VAT control account for the year ended 31 March 20-8. Use the figures given on the previous page.

Note: the business is not charged VAT on its travel expenses.

VAT control account

		Balance b/d	1,470

3 Sole trader financial statements

3.1 A statement of profit or loss shows a profit for the year of £14,900. It is discovered that no allowance has been made for advertising expenses accrued of £620 and rent prepaid of £450 at the year end. What is the adjusted profit for the year?

✔

£14,730	
£15,070	
£15,970	
£13,830	

3.2 Identify whether the following items will be stated in the year end statement of profit or loss as income or expense by putting a tick in the relevant column of the table below.

✔

Item	Income	Expense
Gain on disposal of non-current asset		
Decrease in allowance for doubtful debts		
Irrecoverable debts		
Discounts allowed		
Depreciation charges		
Commission received		

3.3 A statement of profit or loss shows a profit for the year of £18,790. The owner of the business wishes to increase the allowance for doubtful debts by £800 and to write off irrecoverable debts of £250. What is the adjusted profit for the year?

	✔
£18,240	
£19,840	
£19,340	
£17,740	

3.4 You have the following trial balance for a sole trader known as Tysoe Trading. All the necessary year end adjustments have been made.

(a) Prepare a statement of profit or loss (on the next page) for the business for the year ended 31 March 20-6.

Tysoe Trading
Trial balance as at 31 March 20-6

	Dr £	Cr £
Accruals		460
Bank	4,610	
Capital		35,500
Closing inventory	10,200	10,200
Depreciation charges	2,500	
Discounts allowed	490	
Drawings	10,300	
General expenses	25,720	
Office equipment at cost	20,400	
Office equipment: accumulated depreciation		6,500
Opening inventory	11,450	
Payroll expenses	29,610	
Prepayments	990	
Purchases	64,330	
Purchases ledger control		10,310
Rent and rates	7,240	
Sales revenue		140,680
Sales ledger control	18,920	
Value Added Tax		3,110
	206,760	206,760

Tysoe Trading Statement of profit or loss for the year ended 31 March 20-6	£	£
Sales revenue		
Cost of sales		
Gross profit		
Less expenses:		
Total expenses		
Profit for the year		

(b) Indicate where accruals of expenses should be shown in the statement of financial position. Tick **ONE** from:

	✔
As a non-current asset	
As a current asset	
As a current liability	
As an addition to capital	

(c) State the meaning of a credit balance for disposal of a non-current asset in a trial balance. Tick **ONE** from:

	✔
The business has made a gain on disposal	
The business has made a loss on disposal	
The asset has been under depreciated	
The asset has been part-exchanged on disposal	

3.5 The following adjusted trial balance has been taken from the books of Rhianna Aitken, who sells kitchenware, as at 31 March 20-1:

	Dr	Cr
	£	£
Sales ledger control	4,110	
Allowance for doubtful debts		880
Allowance for doubtful debts: adjustment	220	
Purchases ledger control		11,490
Value Added Tax		1,720
Bank		2,360
Capital		27,500
Sales revenue		166,240
Purchases	85,330	
Opening inventory	18,890	
Shop wages	35,560	
Prepayment of shop wages	440	
Heat and light	2,680	
Rent and rates	10,570	
Accrual of rent and rates		590
Shop fittings at cost	36,000	
Shop fittings: depreciation charges	4,750	
Shop fittings: accumulated depreciation		12,380
Disposal of non-current asset		600
Irrecoverable debts	150	
Drawings	25,060	
Closing inventory	22,450	22,450
	246,210	246,210

You are to prepare the financial statements of Rhianna Aitken for the year ended 31 March 20-1, using the conventional format.

4 Partnership financial statements

4.1 A partnership may choose to over-ride some or all of the accounting rules in the Partnership Act 1890 by the partners entering into a separate:

	✔
Appropriation account	
Accounting policy	
Partnership agreement	
Loan agreement	

4.2 Profits of a two-person partnership are £32,100 before the following are taken into account:

- interest on partners' capital accounts, £1,800
- salary of one partner, £10,000
- interest on partners' drawings £700

If the remaining profits are shared equally, how much will each partner receive?

	✔
£10,500	
£11,400	
£12,300	
£16,400	

4.3   You have the following information about a partnership business:

- The financial year ends on 31 March.
- The partners are Uma, Val and Win.
- Partners' annual salaries:

Uma	£10,400
Val	£15,200
Win	£16,750

- Partners' capital account balances as at 31 March 20-4:

Uma	£20,000
Val	£35,000
Win	£15,000

Interest on capital is allowed at 4% per annum on the capital account balance at the end of the financial year.

- Interest charged on partners' drawings:

Uma	£240
Val	£360
Win	£290

- The partners share the remaining profit of £18,000 as follows:

Uma	30%
Val	50%
Win	20%

- Partners' drawings for the year:

Uma	£14,400
Val	£23,600
Win	£18,200

Prepare the current accounts for the partners for the year ended 31 March 20-4. Show clearly the balances carried down. You MUST enter zeros where appropriate. Do NOT use brackets, minus signs or dashes.

Current accounts

	Uma £	Val £	Win £		Uma £	Val £	Win £
Balance b/d	0	0	300	Balance b/d	1,200	700	0

4.4 This Activity is about preparing a partnership statement of financial position.

You are preparing the statement of financial position for the RS Partnership as at 31 March 20-3. The partners are Ros and Sam.

All the necessary year end adjustments have been made, except for the transfer of profit to the current accounts of the partners.

Before sharing profits the balances of the partners' current accounts are:

- Ros £500 credit

- Sam £250 debit

Each partner is entitled to £5,500 profit share.

(a) Calculate the balance of each partner's current account after sharing profits. Indicate whether these balances are DEBIT or CREDIT.

Current account: Ros £	DEBIT / CREDIT
Current account: Sam £	DEBIT / CREDIT

Note: these balances will need to be transferred into the statement of financial position of the partnership which follows.

You have the following trial balance. All the necessary year end adjustments have been made.

(b) Prepare a statement of financial position for the partnership as at 31 March 20-3. You need to use the partners' current account balances that you have just calculated in (a). Do NOT use brackets, minus signs or dashes.

RS Partnership
Trial balance as at 31 March 20-3

	Dr £	Cr £
Accruals		230
Administration expenses	22,680	
Allowance for doubtful debts		670
Allowance for doubtful debts: adjustment		120
Bank	8,910	
Capital account – Ros		30,000
Capital account – Sam		25,000
Cash	490	
Closing inventory	11,670	11,670
Current account – Ros		500
Current account – Sam	250	
Depreciation charges	2,500	
Disposal of non-current asset		300
Office equipment at cost	32,000	
Office equipment: accumulated depreciation		7,900
Opening inventory	10,430	
Purchases	90,850	
Purchases ledger control		13,370
Rent and rates	5,280	
Sales revenue		130,650
Sales ledger control	37,310	
Value Added Tax		1,960
Total	222,370	222,370

RS Partnership

Statement of financial position as at 31 March 20-3

	Cost £	Accumulated depreciation £	Carrying amount £
Non-current assets			
Current assets			
Current liabilities			
Net current assets			
Net assets			
Financed by:	Ros	Sam	Total

5   Changes in partnerships

5.1   Mia, Nell and Olly are in partnership sharing profits equally. Mia is to retire and it is agreed that goodwill is worth £30,000. After Mia's retirement, Nell and Olly will continue to run the partnership and will share profits equally. What will be the goodwill adjustments to Nell's capital account?

	✔
Debit £10,000; credit £10,000	
Debit £10,000; credit £15,000	
Debit £15,000; credit £15,000	
Debit £15,000; credit £10,000	

5.2   Norman and Oliver are in partnership sharing profits equally. Each has a capital account with a balance of £75,000. Peter joins as a new partner. The profit share will be Norman 40%, Oliver 40% and Peter 20%. An adjustment is made for goodwill on the admission of Peter to the value of £40,000, but no goodwill is to be left in the accounts. What will be the balance of Oliver's capital account after the creation and elimination of goodwill?

	✔
£71,000	
£79,000	
£91,000	
£95,000	

5.3 You have the following information about a partnership:

> The partners are Sue and Tom.
>
> • Uma was admitted to the partnership on 1 April 20-3 when she paid £25,000 into the bank account as her capital.
>
> • Profit share, effective until 31 March 20-3:
>   – Sue   60%
>   – Tom   40%
>
> • Profit share, effective from 1 April 20-3:
>   – Sue   50%
>   – Tom   30%
>   – Uma   20%
>
> • Goodwill was valued at £30,000 on 31 March 20-3.
>
> • Goodwill is to be introduced into the partners' capital accounts on 31 March and then eliminated on 1 April.

(a) Prepare the goodwill account of the partnership, showing clearly the transactions on the admission of Uma, the new partner.

Goodwill account

(b) Prepare the capital account for Uma, the new partner, showing clearly the balance carried down as at 1 April 20-3.

Capital account – Uma

		Balance b/d	0

(c)   Identify whether the following statements about the partnership of Sue, Tom and Uma are true or false by putting a tick in the relevant column of the table below.

✔

Statement	True	False
Sue and Tom have each paid money to Uma when she joined the partnership		
The goodwill of £30,000 is kept in a separate bank account, in accordance with the requirements of the Partnership Act 1890		
Uma has paid a premium for a 20% share of the profits of the partnership		
With goodwill valued at £30,000, Sue and Tom will each have £15,000 extra profit this year		

5.4 You have the following information about a partnership business:

> - The financial year ends on 31 March.
>
> - The partners at the beginning of the year were Jim and Kit.
>
> - Leo was admitted to the partnership on 1 January 20-5.
>
> - There is no interest on partners' capital.
>
> - Partners' annual salaries:
>
>   - Jim   £20,000
>
>   - Kit   £18,000
>
>   - Leo   £10,000
>
> - Partners' interest on drawings:
>
>   - Jim   £500 per full year
>
>   - Kit   £300 per full year
>
>   - Leo   £200 per full year
>
> - Profit share, effective until 31 December 20-4:
>
>   - Jim   60%
>
>   - Kit   40%
>
> - Profit share, effective from 1 January 20-5:
>
>   - Jim   50%
>
>   - Kit   30%
>
>   - Leo   20%

Profit for the year ended 31 March 20-5 was £64,000. The profits accrued evenly during the year.

Prepare the appropriation account (on the next page) for the partnership for the year ended 31 March 20-5.

Partnership appropriation account for the year ended 31 March 20-5

	1 Apr 20-4 - 31 Dec 20-4 £	1 Jan 20-5 - 31 Mar 20-5 £	Total £
Profit			
Salaries:			
Jim			
Kit			
Leo			
Interest on drawings:			
Jim			
Kit			
Leo			
Profit available for distribution			

Profit share			
Jim			
Kit			
Leo			
Total profit distributed			

Chapter activities answers

1 Preparing financial statements

1.1 Opening inventory + purchases − closing inventory

1.2 Statement of profit or loss

1.3 The excess of current assets over current liabilities

1.4 Business A: gross profit £8,000, profit for year £4,000

Business B: gross profit £17,000, expenses £7,000

Business C: sales £36,500, profit for year £6,750

Business D: purchases £25,500, expenses £9,800

Business E: opening inventory £8,350, loss for year £1,700

Business F: closing inventory £4,600, expenses £15,000

1.5

(a)   £53,220

(b)

	Debit	Credit	No change
Non-current assets	✔		
Trade receivables			✔
Trade payables			✔
Bank		✔	
Capital			✔

(c)   A bank loan repayable in two years' time

1.6

MATT SMITH

STATEMENT OF PROFIT OR LOSS
for the year ended 31 December 20-4

	£	£
Sales revenue		259,688
Opening inventory	14,350	
Purchases	114,472	
	128,822	
Less Closing inventory	16,280	
Cost of sales		112,542
Gross profit		147,146
Less expenses:		
Rent and rates	13,718	
Heating and lighting	12,540	
Payroll expenses	42,614	
Vehicle expenses	5,817	
Advertising	6,341	
		81,030
Profit for the year		66,116

---

continued

STATEMENT OF FINANCIAL POSITION as at 31 December 20-4

	£	£	£
Non-current assets			
Premises at cost			75,000
Office equipment at cost			33,000
Vehicles at cost			21,500
			129,500
Current assets			
Inventory (closing)		16,280	
Trade receivables		23,854	
Bank		1,235	
Cash		125	
		41,494	
Less Current liabilities			
Trade payables	14,258		
Value Added Tax	5,478		
		19,736	
Net current assets			21,758
			151,258
Less Non-current liabilities			
Loan from bank			35,000
NET ASSETS			116,258
FINANCED BY			
Capital			
Opening capital			62,500
Add Profit for the year			66,116
			128,616
Less Drawings			12,358
Closing capital			116,258

1.7

LISA JAMES
STATEMENT OF PROFIT OR LOSS
for the year ended 31 March 20-7

	£	£	£
Sales revenue			127,500
Less Sales returns			2,150
Net sales revenue			125,350
Opening inventory		17,540	
Purchases	77,200		
Add Carriage in	680		
	77,880		
Less Purchases returns	3,040		
Net purchases		74,840	
		92,380	
Less Closing inventory		19,960	
Cost of sales			72,420
Gross profit			52,930
Add income: Discount received			230
			53,160
Less expenses:			
Discount allowed		470	
Carriage out		1,540	
Other expenses		35,830	
			37,840
Profit for the year			15,320

2   Incomplete records accounting

2.1   £375,000

Workings: £250,000 + £125,000 profit

2.2   £145,000

Workings: cost of sales = £140,000 + closing inventory £20,000 = £160,000 – opening inventory £15,000

2.3   £19,500

Workings: £16,400 + £73,400 – £68,100 – £1,800 – £400

2.4

TALIB ZABBAR CALCULATION OF INVENTORY LOSS FOR THE YEAR ENDED 31 MARCH 20-2		
	£	£
Opening inventory		30,500
Purchases		89,500
Cost of inventory available for sale		120,000
Sales	160,000	
Less Normal gross sales margin (40%)	64,000	
Cost of sales		96,000
Estimated closing inventory		24,000
Less Actual closing inventory		21,500
Value of inventory loss		2,500

2.5 **(a)** **Sales ledger control account**

Balance b/d	16,250	Sales returns day book	2,160
Sales day book	122,400	Bank	117,950
		Discounts allowed	430
		Balance c/d	18,110
	138,650		138,650

(b) **Purchases ledger control account**

Purchases returns day book	1,488	Balance b/d	10,380
Bank	72,833	Purchases day book	76,800
Balance c/d	12,859		
	87,180		87,180

(c) **VAT control account**

Purchases day book	12,800	Balance b/d	1,470
Sales returns day book	360	Sales day book	20,400
Administration expenses	4,400	Purchases returns day book	248
Bank	2,760		
Balance c/d	1,798		
	22,118		22,118

3 Sole trader financial statements

3.1 £14,730

3.2

Item	Income	Expense
Gain on disposal of non-current asset	✔	
Decrease in allowance for doubtful debts	✔	
Irrecoverable debts		✔
Discounts allowed		✔
Depreciation charges		✔
Commission received	✔	

3.3 £17,740

3.4 **(a)**

Tysoe Trading Statement of profit or loss for the year ended 31 March 20-6		
	£	£
Sales revenue		140,680
Opening inventory	11,450	
Purchases	64,330	
Less: Closing inventory	10,200	
Cost of sales		65,580
Gross profit		75,100
Less expenses:		
Depreciation charges	2,500	
Discounts allowed	490	
General expenses	25,720	
Payroll expenses	29,610	
Rent and rates	7,240	
Total expenses		65,560
Profit for the year		9,540

(b) As a current liability

(c) The business has made a gain on disposal

3.5

RHIANNA AITKEN
STATEMENT OF PROFIT OR LOSS
for the year ended 31 March 20-1

	£	£
Sales revenue		166,240
Opening inventory	18,890	
Purchases	85,330	
	104,220	
Less Closing inventory	22,450	
Cost of sales		81,770
Gross profit		84,470
Add income:		
Gain on disposal of non-current asset		600
		85,070
Less expenses:		
Allowance for doubtful debts: adjustment	220	
Shop wages	35,560	
Heat and light	2,680	
Rent and rates	10,570	
Depreciation charges: shop fittings	4,750	
Irrecoverable debts	150	
		53,930
Profit for the year		31,140

STATEMENT OF FINANCIAL POSITION
as at 31 March 20-1

	£ Cost	£ Accumulated depreciation	£ Carrying amount
Non-current assets			
Shop fittings	36,000	12,380	23,620
Current assets			
Inventory		22,450	
Trade receivables		*3,230	
		3,230	
Prepayment of expenses		440	
		26,120	
Less Current liabilities			
Trade payables	11,490		
Value Added Tax	1,720		
Accrual of expenses	590		
Bank	2,360		
		16,160	
Net current assets			9,960
NET ASSETS			33,580
FINANCED BY			
Capital			
Opening capital			27,500
Add Profit for the year			31,140
			58,640
Less Drawings			25,060
Closing capital			33,580

* sales ledger control £4,110 *minus* allowance for doubtful debts £880

4 Partnership financial statements

4.1 Partnership agreement

4.2 £10,500

4.3

Current accounts

	Uma £	Val £	Win £		Uma £	Val £	Win £
Balance b/d	0	0	300	Balance b/d	1,200	700	0
Drawings	14,400	23,600	18,200	Salaries	10,400	15,200	16,750
Interest on drawings	240	360	290	Interest on capital	800	1,400	600
Balance c/d	3,160	2,340	2,160	Profit share	5,400	9,000	3,600
	17,800	26,300	20,950		17,800	26,300	20,950

4.4 **(a)**   Current account: Ros £6,000 CREDIT

Current account: Sam £5,250 CREDIT

(b)   **RS Partnership**

Statement of financial position as at 31 March 20-3

	Cost £	Accumulated depreciation £	Carrying amount £
Non-current assets			
Office equipment	32,000	7,900	24,100
Current assets			
Inventory		11,670	
Trade receivables		*36,640	
Bank		8,910	
Cash		490	
		57,710	
Current liabilities			
Trade payables	13,370		
Value Added Tax	1,960		
Accruals	230		
		15,560	
Net current assets			42,150
Net assets			66,250
Financed by:	Ros	Sam	Total
Capital accounts	30,000	25,000	55,000
Current accounts	6,000	5,250	11,250
	36,000	30,250	66,250

* sales ledger control £37,310 *minus* allowance for doubtful debts £670

Note: bank £8,910 + cash £490 = cash and cash equivalents £9,400

5 | Changes in partnerships

5.1   Debit £15,000; credit £10,000

5.2   £79,000

Workings: £75,000 + (£40,000 x 50%) − (£40,000 x 40%)

5.3   **(a)**   **Goodwill account**

Capital – Sue	18,000	Capital – Sue	15,000
Capital – Tom	12,000	Capital – Tom	9,000
		Capital – Uma	6,000
	30,000		30,000

(b)   **Capital account – Uma**

Goodwill	6,000	Balance b/d	0
Balance c/d	19,000	Bank	25,000
	25,000		25,000

(c)

Statement	True	False
Sue and Tom have each paid money to Uma when she joined the partnership		✔
The goodwill of £30,000 is kept in a separate bank account, in accordance with the requirements of the Partnership Act 1890		✔
Uma has paid a premium for a 20% share of the profits of the partnership	✔	
With goodwill valued at £30,000, Sue and Tom will each have £15,000 extra profit this year		✔

5.4

Partnership appropriation account for the year ended 31 March 20-5

	1 Apr 20-4 - 31 Dec 20-4 £	1 Jan 20-5 - 31 Mar 20-5 £	Total £
Profit	48,000	16,000	64,000
Salaries:			
Jim	15,000	5,000	20,000
Kit	13,500	4,500	18,000
Leo	0	2,500	2,500
Interest on drawings:			
Jim	375	125	500
Kit	225	75	300
Leo	0	50	50
Profit available for distribution	20,100	4,250	24,350

Note: interest on drawings is *added* to profit (because it is charged to the partners).

Profit share	£	£	£
Jim	12,060	2,125	14,185
Kit	8,040	1,275	9,315
Leo	0	850	850
Total profit distributed	20,100	4,250	24,350

Practice assessment 1

Task 1

This task is about incomplete records and reconstructing general ledger accounts.

You are working on the accounting records of a sole trader for the year ended 31 March 20-1. You have the following information:

Day book summaries for the year	Net £	VAT £	Total £
Sales	134,000	26,800	160,800
Sales returns	2,400	480	2,880
Purchases	82,000	16,400	98,400
Purchases returns	1,600	320	1,920

Note: all sales and purchases are on credit terms.

Further information	Net £	VAT £	Total £
Office expenses	20,600	4,120	24,720

Note: office expenses are not included in the purchases day book.

Bank summary	Dr £		Cr £
Balance b/d	10,770	Office expenses	24,720
Trade receivables	152,490	Trade payables	92,845
Balance c/d	3,400	HMRC for VAT	5,245
		Drawings	17,500
		Payroll expenses	26,350
	166,660		166,660

Further information:
- Cash (settlement) discounts received during the year were £550.
- Cash (settlement) discounts allowed during the year were £230.

Select your entries from the following list:

Balance b/d, Balance c/d, Bank, Cash purchases, Cash sales, Discounts allowed, Discounts received, Drawings, Inventory, Loan, Office expenses, Payroll expenses, Purchases day book, Purchases returns day book, Sales day book, Sales returns day book, Value Added Tax.

(a)   Using the figures given on the previous page, prepare the sales ledger control account for the year ended 31 March 20-1. Show clearly the amount of trade receivables at the year end as the balance carried down.

Sales ledger control account

Balance b/d	18,275		

(b)   Using the figures given on the previous page, prepare the purchases ledger control account for the year ended 31 March 20-1. Show clearly the amount of trade payables at the year end as the balance carried down.

Purchases ledger control account

		Balance b/d	10,365

(c)   Using the figures given on page 44, prepare the VAT control account for the year ended 31 March 20-1. Show clearly the amount of VAT due to HM Revenue & Customs at the year end as the balance carried down.

VAT control account

		Balance b/d	2,140

Task 2

This task is about calculating missing balances and the preparation of financial statements.

You have the following information about a sole trader. The value of assets and liabilities as at 1 April 20-1 was:

• Inventory	£14,270
• Bank (overdrawn)	£3,210
• Trade payables	£6,180
• Non-current assets at carrying amount	£25,500
• Bank loan	£12,500
• Trade receivables	£9,450

There were no other assets or liabilities.

(a) Calculate the following as at 1 April 20-1. Do NOT enter any figures as negative.

Assets   £

Liabilities £

Capital   £

For the year ended 31 March 20-1 you have the following information:

• Trade payables at 1 April 20-0	£7,240
• Trade payables at 31 March 20-1	£6,180
• Bank payments to trade payables during the year	£51,420
• Cash purchases during the year	£1,730

(b) Calculate the purchases for the year ended 31 March 20-1.

£

(c)   Which of the following best describes goodwill? Tick **ONE** answer.

	✔
A liability, where payment is due in more than one year's time	
An intangible non-current asset which does not have material substance	
A short-term asset which changes regularly	
A tangible non-current asset which has material substance	

You are now working on the accounts of a different business. This business recently had a fire in its offices and the computer on which the accounting records are kept, together with the majority of the supporting paperwork and computer backups were destroyed.

The business makes all its sales in cash.

You have been asked to produce some figures for the financial statements.

Each source of information below will help find some of the figures that are missing.

(d)   For each source of information indicate the **ONE** missing figure that it will help to find. Put a tick in the relevant column of the table below.

Note: you do not have sufficient information to find all of the missing figures.

					✔
Source of information	**Missing figures**				
	Total sales	**Total purchases**	**Closing inventory**	**Profit for the year**	**Non-current assets**
Bank statement					
Physical inventory count					
Gross sales margin					

Task 3

This task is about preparing the financial statements for sole traders.

You have the following trial balance for a sole trader known as Tairo Trading. All the necessary year end adjustments have been made.

The following accounting policy is used by Tairo Trading:

- Sales revenue should include sales returns, if any.

(a)   Calculate the sales revenue figure to be included in the statement of profit or loss for Tairo Trading.

£ [   ]

(b)   Prepare a statement of profit or loss for Tairo Trading for the year ended 31 March 20-1.

If necessary, use a minus sign to indicate ONLY the following:
- the deduction of an account balance used to make up cost of sales (cost of goods sold)
- a loss for the year

Tairo Trading Trial balance as at 31 March 20-1		
	Dr	**Cr**
	£	**£**
Accruals		540
Allowance for doubtful debts		1,000
Allowance for doubtful debts adjustment		100
Bank		1,270
Capital		30,180
Closing inventory	8,350	8,350
Depreciation charges	6,240	
Discounts allowed	350	
Drawings	11,970	
General expenses	13,860	
Opening inventory	6,290	
Payroll expenses	28,450	
Prepayments	330	
Purchases	93,760	
Purchases ledger control		10,850
Rent and rates	10,390	
Sales revenue		160,830
Sales ledger control	22,820	
Sales returns	900	
Value Added Tax		5,640
Vehicles accumulated depreciation		10,250
Vehicles at cost	25,300	
	229,010	229,010

Select your entries from the following list:

Accruals, Allowance for doubtful debts, Allowance for doubtful debts adjustment, Bank, Capital, Closing inventory, Depreciation charges, Discounts allowed, Drawings, General expenses, Opening inventory, Payroll expenses, Prepayments, Purchases, Purchases ledger control, Rent and rates, Sales revenue, Sales ledger control, Sales returns, Value Added Tax, Vehicles accumulated depreciation, Vehicles at cost.

Tairo Trading Statement of profit or loss for the year ended 31 March 20-1	£	£
Sales revenue		
Cost of sales		
Gross profit		
Add:		
Less:		
Total expenses		
Profit/loss for the year		

(c)   Indicate where prepayment of expenses should be shown in the statement of financial position.
Tick **ONE** from:

	✔
As a non-current asset	
As a current asset	
As a current liability	
As a non-current liability	

·**(d)**   Which of the following regarding the financial statements of a sole trader is TRUE? Choose
ONE option.

	✔
Drawings are added to capital in the statement of financial position	
Drawings are added to expenses in the statement of profit or loss	
Drawings are added to current liabilities in the statement of financial position	
Drawings are deducted from capital in the statement of financial position	

Task 4

This task is about accounting for partnerships.

You have the following information:

- The partners are Kay, Lee and Matt.

- Kay is to retire from the partnership on 1 April 20-1. Lee and Matt will continue in partnership. Kay agrees to leave £25,000 of the amount due to her as a loan to the new partnership; the remainder will be paid to her from the partnership bank account.

- Profit share, effective until 31 March 20-1:
  - Kay   40%
  - Lee   40%
  - Matt   20%

- Profit share, effective from 1 April 20-1:
  - Lee   50%
  - Matt   50%

- Goodwill was valued at £30,000 on 31 March 20-1.

- Goodwill is to be introduced into the accounting records on 31 March and then eliminated on 1 April.

(a) Prepare the capital account for Kay, the partner who is retiring, showing clearly the amount to be paid to her from the partnership bank account as at 1 April 20-1.

Select your entries from the following list:

Balance b/d, Balance c/d, Bank, Capital – Kay, Capital – Lee, Capital – Matt, Current – Kay, Current – Lee, Current – Matt, Drawings, Goodwill, Loan.

Capital account – Kay

	£		£
		Balance b/d	48,500

(b) Identify whether the following statements about a partnership agreement are true or false by putting a tick in the relevant column of the table below.

✔

Statement	True	False
All partnership agreements state that profits and losses must be shared equally between the partners		
A partnership agreement will state the salaries to be paid to employees		
A partnership agreement may state that interest is to be allowed on partners' capitals, and at what rate		
A partnership agreement may state that interest is to be charged on partners' drawings, and at what rate		

You have the following information about another partnership business:

- The financial year ends on 31 March.

- The partners at the beginning of the year were Jane and Kate.

- Lysa was admitted to the partnership on 1 July 20-0.

- Partners' annual salaries:
    - Jane   £20,000
    - Kate   £24,000
    - Lysa   nil

- Partners' interest on capital:
    - Jane   £1,200 per full year
    - Kate   £1,800 per full year
    - Lysa   £400 per full year

- Profit share, effective until 30 June 20-0:
    - Jane   60%
    - Kate   40%

- Profit share, effective from 1 July 20-0:
    - Jane   50%
    - Kate   30%
    - Lysa   20%

- Profit for the year ended 31 March 20-1 was £68,000. The profits accrued evenly during the year.

(c)   Prepare the appropriation account for the partnership business for the year ended 31 March 20-1.

- You MUST enter zeros where appropriate.
- Do NOT use brackets, minus signs or dashes.

Partnership appropriation account for the year ended 31 March 20-1

	1 April 20-0 – 30 June 20-0 £	1 July 20-0 – 31 March 20-1 £	Total £
Profit for appropriation			
Salaries:			
Jane			
Kate			
Lysa			
Interest on capital:			
Jane			
Kate			
Lysa			
Profit available for distribution			

Profit share			
Jane			
Kate			
Lysa			
Total profit distributed			

Task 5

This task is about preparing a partnership statement of financial position.

You are preparing the statement of financial position for the Beacon Partnership as at 31 March 20-1. The partners are Yulia and Zoe.

All the necessary year end adjustments have been made, except for the transfer of profit to the current accounts of the partners.

Before sharing profits the balances of the partners' current accounts are:

- Yulia £950 debit

- Zoe   £450 credit

Each partner is entitled to £5,250 profit share.

(a)   Calculate the balance of each partner's current account after sharing profits. Indicate whether these balances are DEBIT or CREDIT.

Current account: Yulia £	DEBIT / CREDIT
Current account: Zoe £	DEBIT / CREDIT

Note: these balances will need to be transferred into the statement of financial position of the partnership which follows.

You have the following trial balance. All the necessary year end adjustments have been made.

(b) Prepare a statement of financial position for the partnership as at 31 March 20-1. You need to use the partners' current account balances that you have just calculated in (a). Do NOT use brackets, minus signs or dashes.

Beacon Partnership
Trial balance as at 31 March 20-1

	Dr £	Cr £
Accruals		690
Administration expenses	20,830	
Allowance for doubtful debts		1,400
Allowance for doubtful debts adjustment	250	
Bank	11,750	
Capital account – Yulia		30,000
Capital account – Zoe		22,000
Cash	220	
Closing inventory	17,380	17,380
Current account – Yulia	950	
Current account – Zoe		450
Depreciation charges	4,650	
Disposal of non-current asset		540
Office equipment at cost	24,400	
Office equipment accumulated depreciation		10,250
Opening inventory	15,140	
Payroll expenses	36,320	
Purchases	85,460	
Purchases ledger control		11,680
Sales revenue		155,230
Sales ledger control	35,380	
Value Added Tax		3,110
Total	252,730	252,730

Select your entries from the following list:

Accruals, Bank, Capital accounts, Cash, Current accounts, Expenses, Inventory, Office equipment, Prepayments, Purchases, Purchases returns, Sales, Sales returns, Trade payables, Trade receivables, Value Added Tax.

Beacon Partnership

Statement of financial position as at 31 March 20-1

	£	£	£
Non-current assets	Cost	Accumulated depreciation	Carrying amount
Current assets			
Total current assets			
Current liabilities			
Total current liabilities			
Net current assets			
Net assets			
Financed by:	Yulia	Zoe	Total

Practice assessment 2

Task 1

This task is about incomplete records and reconstructing general ledger accounts.

You are working on the accounting records of a sole trader for the year ended 31 March 20-1. You have the following information:

Day book summaries for the year	Net £	VAT £	Total £
Sales	154,000	30,800	184,800
Purchases	86,000	17,200	103,200

Note: all sales and purchases are on credit terms. There were no sales and purchases returns during the year.

Further information	Net £	VAT £	Total £
Administration expenses	20,300	4,060	24,360

Notes:

· administration expenses are not included in the purchases day book

· all administration expenses have been paid from the bank during the year

Balances as at:	31 March 20-0 £	31 March 20-1 £
Trade receivables	28,200	29,400
Trade payables	12,600	13,350
VAT (payable)	3,290	4,150

Further information:

· Cash (settlement) discounts allowed during the year were £490.

· Cash (settlement) discounts received during the year were £305.

· Bank receipts from trade receivables during the year were £183,110.

· Payroll expenses paid during the year were £25,490.

· Drawings from the bank during the year were £16,300.

· There were no other bank receipts or payments during the year.

Select your entries from the following list:

Administration expenses, Balance b/d, Balance c/d, Bank, Cash purchases, Cash sales, Discounts allowed, Discounts received, Drawings, Inventory, Payroll expenses, Purchases day book, Purchases ledger control, Purchases returns day book, Sales day book, Sales ledger control, Sales returns day book, Value Added Tax.

(a)   Using the figures given on the previous page, prepare the purchases ledger control account for the year ended 31 March 20-1. Show clearly bank payments to trade payables as the balancing figure.

Purchases ledger control account

(b)   Using the figures given on the previous page, prepare the VAT control account for the year ended 31 March 20-1. Show clearly bank payments for Value Added Tax as the balancing figure.

VAT control account

(c) Find the closing balance for bank by preparing the bank account summary for the year ended 31 March 20-1. Use the figures given on page 60.

Bank account

		Balance b/d	2,430

Task 2

This task is about calculating missing balances and the preparation of financial statements.

The capital account balance of a sole trader at 1 April 20-0 was £35,600.

For the year ended 31 March 20-1:

· profit was £16,900

· drawings from the bank were £13,300

· goods taken for own use were £750

(a) Calculate the capital account balance as at 31 March 20-1.

£

(b) Tick the boxes to classify the following items as non-current assets, current assets, current liabilities or non-current liabilities. You must choose **ONE** answer for **EACH** line.

	Non-current assets	Current assets	Current liabilities	Non-current liabilities
Office equipment				
Inventory				
Bank loan				
Trade receivables				
Goodwill				

You are given the following information about a sole trader business for the year ended 31 March 20-1:

· sales for the year are £400,000

· the gross sales margin is 25%

· inventory at 1 April 20-0 is £38,000

· inventory at 31 March 20-1 is £45,000

(c) Calculate the purchases for the year ended 31 March 20-1.

£

You are now working on the accounts of a different business. Full accounting records have not been kept and you have been asked to produce some figures for the financial statements.

The business makes all its sales in cash.

The figures you need to calculate and the sources of the information available to you are given below.

(d) For each missing figure indicate the **ONE** source of information that will help you. Put a tick in the relevant column of the table below.

✔

Missing figures	Source of information			
	Bank statement	Physical inventory count	Trade receivables	Gross sales margin
Closing inventory				
Cash sales				
Total purchases				

Task 3

This task is about preparing financial statements for sole traders.

You have the following trial balance for a sole trader known as Dracus Trading. All the necessary year end adjustments have been made.

The following accounting policy is used by Dracus Trading:

- Purchases should include purchases returns, if any.

(a) Calculate the purchases figure to be included in the statement of profit or loss for Dracus Trading.

£

(b) Prepare a statement of profit or loss for Dracus Trading for the year ended 31 March 20-1.

If necessary, use a minus sign to indicate ONLY the following:

- the deduction of an account balance used to make up cost of sales (cost of goods sold)
- a loss for the year

Dracus Trading Trial balance as at 31 March 20-1		
	Dr	**Cr**
	£	**£**
Accruals		240
Bank		2,480
Capital		37,110
Closing inventory	18,190	18,190
Depreciation charges	7,240	
Discounts received		230
Drawings	15,540	
Office equipment at cost	20,730	
Office equipment accumulated depreciation		6,250
Opening inventory	17,420	
Payroll expenses	56,890	
Payroll liabilities		550
Prepayments	450	
Purchases	141,080	
Purchases ledger control		15,380
Purchases returns		350
Rent and rates	16,780	
Sales revenue		240,340
Sales ledger control	33,640	
Value Added Tax		6,840
	327,960	327,960

Select your entries from the following list:

Accruals, Bank, Capital, Closing inventory, Depreciation charges, Discounts received, Drawings, Office equipment at cost, Office equipment accumulated depreciation, Opening inventory, Payroll expenses, Payroll liabilities, Prepayments, Purchases, Purchases ledger control, Purchases returns, Rent and rates, Sales revenue, Sales ledger control, Value Added Tax.

Dracus Trading **Statement of profit or loss for the year ended 31 March 20-1**	£	£
Sales revenue		
Cost of sales		
Gross profit		
Add:		
Less:		
Total expenses		
Profit/loss for the year		

(c)   Where should a bank overdraft be shown in the statement of financial position? Tick **ONE** from:

	✔
As a non-current asset	
As a current asset	
As a current liability	
As a non-current liability	

(d)   Which of the following is best described as a non-current liability?

	✔
A bank loan repayable in two years' time	
Trade payables	
A bank overdraft	
Payroll liabilities	

(e)   Identify whether the following statements about a two-column trial balance are true or false by putting a tick in the relevant column of the table below.

Statement	True	False
A trial balance which balances proves that no errors have been made in the double-entry		
A trial balance gives a profit figure		
The closing inventory is recognised in both columns of the trial balance, except when it is included in a cost of sales account		
A trial balance distinguishes between the figures that relate to the statement of profit or loss and the figures that relate to the statement of financial position		

Task 4

This task is about accounting for partnerships.

You have the following information:

> • The financial year ends on 31 March.
>
> • The partners are Freya and Gina.
>
> • Profit share, effective until 30 September 20-0:
>   – Freya 50%
>   – Gina 50%
>
> • Profit share, effective from 1 October 20-0:
>   – Freya 40%
>   – Gina 60%
>
> • Goodwill was valued at £30,000 on 30 September 20-0.
>
> • Goodwill is to be introduced into the partners' capital accounts on 30 September and then eliminated on 1 October.

(a) Prepare the partners' capital accounts to record the change in profit share, showing clearly the balance carried down.

Select your entries from the following list:

Balance b/d, Balance c/d, Bank, Capital – Freya, Capital – Gina, Current – Freya, Current – Gina, Drawings, Goodwill.

Partners' capital accounts

	Freya £	Gina £		Freya £	Gina £
			Balances b/d	24,000	36,000

(b) Identify how the following partnership transactions will be recorded in the accounts – whether capital or current account, and whether debit or credit. Indicate your answer by putting a tick in the relevant column of the table below.

Transaction	Capital account		Current account	
	Dr ✔	Cr ✔	Dr ✔	Cr ✔
Capital introduced				
Partner's salary				
Drawings				
Goodwill created				
Share of profits				
Interest on capital				

You have the following information about another partnership business:

- The financial year ends on 31 March.

- The partners are Rob, Sue and Tom.

- Partners' annual salaries:
Rob	£10,840
Sue	£13,690
Tom	£10,900

- Partners' capital account balances as at 31 March 20-1:
Rob	£50,000
Sue	£70,000
Tom	£30,000

  Interest on capital is allowed at 2% per annum on the capital account balance at the end of the financial year.

- The partners share the remaining profit of £22,000 as follows:
Rob	25%
Sue	60%
Tom	15%

- Partners' drawings for the year:
Rob	£16,200
Sue	£25,900
Tom	£14,600

- Interest charged on partners' drawings for the year:
Rob	£250
Sue	£325
Tom	£300

(c)   Prepare the current accounts for the partners for the year ended 31 March 20-1. Show clearly the balances carried down.

- You MUST enter zeros where appropriate.

- Do NOT use brackets, minus signs or dashes.

Select your entries from the following list:

Balance b/d, Balance c/d, Bank, Capital – Rob, Capital – Sue, Capital – Tom, Current – Rob, Current – Sue, Current – Tom, Drawings, Goodwill, Interest on capital, Interest on drawings, Salaries, Share of loss, Share of profit.

Current accounts

	Rob £	Sue £	Tom £		Rob £	Sue £	Tom £
Balance b/d	0	0	250	Balance b/d	650	1,200	0

Task 5

This task is about preparing a partnership statement of financial position.

You are preparing the statement of financial position for the Sarton Partnership as at 31 March 20-1. The partners are Sara and Toni.

All the necessary year end adjustments have been made, except for the transfer of profit to the current accounts of the partners.

Before sharing profits the balances of the partners' current accounts are:

- Sara £620 credit

- Toni £140 debit

Each partner is entitled to £3,500 profit share.

(a) Calculate the balance of each partner's current account after sharing profits. Indicate whether these balances are DEBIT or CREDIT.

Current account: Sara £	DEBIT / CREDIT
Current account: Toni £	DEBIT / CREDIT

Note: these balances will need to be transferred into the statement of financial position of the partnership which follows.

You have the following trial balance. All the necessary year end adjustments have been made.

(b) Prepare a statement of financial position for the partnership as at 31 March 20-1. You need to use the partners' current account balances that you have just calculated in (a). Do NOT use brackets, minus signs or dashes.

Sarton Partnership
Trial balance as at 31 March 20-1

	Dr £	Cr £
Accruals		400
Administration expenses	16,210	
Allowance for doubtful debts		830
Allowance for doubtful debts adjustment	120	
Bank	10,330	
Capital account – Sara		15,000
Capital account – Toni		12,500
Closing inventory	6,090	6,090
Current account – Sara		620
Current account – Toni	140	
Depreciation charge	4,750	
Disposal of non-current asset		160
Opening inventory	5,150	
Prepayments	440	
Purchases	45,930	
Purchases ledger control		6,420
Sales revenue		85,320
Sales ledger control	10,360	
Selling expenses	12,410	
Value Added Tax		1,290
Vehicles at cost	29,500	
Vehicles accumulated depreciation		12,800
Total	141,430	141,430

Select your entries from the following list:

Accruals, Bank, Capital accounts, Cash, Current accounts, Expenses, Inventory, Prepayments, Purchases, Purchases returns, Sales, Sales returns, Trade payables, Trade receivables, Value Added Tax, Vehicles.

Sarton Partnership

Statement of financial position as at 31 March 20-1

	£	£	£
Non-current assets	Cost	Accumulated depreciation	Carrying amount
Current assets			
Total current assets			
Current liabilities			
Total current liabilities			
Net current assets			
Net assets			
Financed by:	Sara	Toni	Total

Practice
assessment 3

Task 1

This task is about incomplete records and reconstructing general ledger accounts.

You are working on the accounting records of a sole trader for the year ended 31 March 20-6.

The business is not registered for VAT.

You have the following information:

Receipts and payments recorded in the bank account include:

	£
Amounts from credit customers	67,031
Amounts to credit suppliers	27,846
Drawings	12,500
Office expenses	19,361
Bank interest paid	247

Balance at:	31 March 20-5	31 March 20-6
	£	£
Trade receivables	8,216	9,047
Trade payables	4,367	4,498
Closing inventory	4,221	4,864
Bank	3,219 credit	1,246 debit

You are also told that:

•   All sales are on credit terms.

•   Sales totalled £68,422 for the year.

Select your entries from the following list:

Allowance for doubtful debts, Allowance for doubtful debts adjustment, Balance b/d, Balance c/d, Bank, Bank interest paid, Capital, Cash purchases, Cash sales, Closing inventory, Credit purchases, Credit sales, Drawings, Irrecoverable debts, Office expenses, Opening inventory, Purchases ledger control, Sales ledger control.

(a)   Find the credit purchases figure by preparing the purchases ledger control account for the year ended 31 March 20-6.

Purchases ledger control account

During the year, a customer was declared bankrupt. The amount has been written off in full.

(b) Find the amount written off by preparing the sales ledger control account for the year ended 31 March 20-6.

Sales ledger control account

(c) Find the cash purchases by preparing a summarised bank account for the year ended 31 March 20-6.

Bank account

		Balance b/d	3,219
		Balance c/d	1,246

Task 2

This task is about calculating missing balances and the preparation of financial statements.

You have the following information about events on 1 April 20-5.

- A sole trader started business.
- The business was not registered for VAT.
- The sole trader transferred £20,000 of her own money into the business bank account.
- £8,000 was paid from this account for a delivery van.
- Goods for resale by the business costing £1,200 were purchased using the trader's personal bank account.

(a) Complete the capital account as at 1 April 20-5, showing clearly the balance carried down.

Select your entries for the details column from the following list:

Balance b/d, Balance c/d, Bank, Delivery van at cost, Drawings, Purchases, Purchases ledger control, Sales, Sales ledger control, Suspense.

Capital account

	£		£
		Balance b/d	0

The following day, the sole trader bought furniture for use in the office at a cost of £1,500. This was paid for from the business bank account and the transaction was entered in the records.

(b) Tick the appropriate boxes to show how this transaction affects the elements of the accounting equation below.

You must choose ONE answer for EACH row.

	Increase	Decrease	No change
Assets			
Liabilities			
Capital			

At the end of the financial year on 31 March 20-6, you have the following further information:

- Total sales were £80,000.
- Total purchases were £67,340.
- A mark-up of 25% on cost was used throughout the year.

(c)   Calculate the value of the cost of goods sold for the year ended 31 March 20-6.

£

(d)   Calculate the value of inventory as at 31 March 20-6.

£

You are given the following information about another sole trader.

- The cash book shows a credit balance of £7,290.
- The bank statement on the same date shows that the business has a debit balance of £5,360.

(e)   Which **ONE** of the following could explain this difference?

✔

Bank charges on the bank statement have not been entered in the cash book	
Cheques to suppliers sent out at the end of the month have not yet cleared	
A BACS/Faster Payments receipt from a trade receivable has been posted to the bank account twice	

Task 3

This task is about preparing financial statements for sole traders.

You have the following trial balance for a sole trader known as Hanslo Trading. All the necessary year end adjustments have been made.

The following are accounting policies used by Hanslo:

- Sales revenue should include sales returns, if any.

- Purchases should include purchases returns and carriage inwards, if any.

(a)   Calculate the sales revenue figure to be included in the statement of profit or loss for Hanslo Trading.

£

(b)   Calculate the purchases figure to be included in the statement of profit or loss for Hanslo Trading.

£

(c)   Prepare a statement of profit or loss for Hanslo Trading for the year ended 31 March 20-6.
If necessary, use a minus sign to indicate ONLY the following:

- the deduction of an account balance used to make up cost of sales (cost of goods
  sold)

- a loss for the year

Hanslo Trading Trial balance as at 31 March 20-6		
	Dr	**Cr**
	£	£
Accruals		740
Bank	4,850	
Capital		65,000
Carriage inwards	1,430	
Carriage outwards	2,790	
Cash	220	
Closing inventory	11,340	11,340
Depreciation charges	4,520	
Disposal of non-current assets		990
Drawings	16,500	
General expenses	23,920	
Opening inventory	9,760	
Payroll expenses	49,050	
Prepayments	1,310	
Purchases	47,860	
Purchases ledger control		7,530
Sales revenue		125,860
Sales ledger control	18,170	
Sales returns	2,160	
Value Added Tax		2,710
Vehicles at cost	35,000	
Vehicles accumulated depreciation		14,710
Total	228,880	228,880

Select your entries from the following list:

Accruals, Bank, Capital, Carriage inwards, Carriage outwards, Cash, Closing inventory, Depreciation charges, Disposal of non-current assets, Drawings, General expenses, Opening inventory, Payroll expenses, Prepayments, Purchases, Purchases ledger control, Sales ledger control, Sales revenue, Sales returns, Value Added Tax, Vehicles at cost, Vehicles accumulated depreciation.

Hanslo Trading Statement of profit or loss for the year ended 31 March 20-6	£	£
Sales revenue		
Cost of sales		
Gross profit		
Add:		
Less:		
Total expenses		
Profit/loss for the year		

(d) Identify the meaning of a debit balance for disposal of non-current assets in a trial balance. Tick **ONE** from:

	✔
The business has made a gain on disposal	
The business has made a loss on disposal	
The asset has been over-depreciated	
The asset has been part-exchanged on disposal	

Task 4

This task is about accounting for partnerships.

You have the following information:

- Hal and Ian have been the owners of a partnership business for many years sharing profits and losses in the ratio 2:1, with Hal receiving the larger share.

- On 1 October 20-5, the partnership agreement was changed so that Hal and Ian will share profits and losses in the ratio 3:2, with Hal receiving the larger share.

- Goodwill was valued at £60,000 at this date and has already been introduced into the partnership accounting records. It now needs to be eliminated.

(a) Show the entries required to eliminate the goodwill from the partnership accounting records on 1 October 20-5.

Select your entries for the 'Account name' column from the following list:

Balance b/d, Balance c/d, Bank, Capital – Hal, Capital – Ian, Current – Hal, Current – Ian, Goodwill.

Account name	Amount £	Debit ✔	Credit ✔

(b) Complete the following statements regarding Hal's position in the partnership at the end of the day on 1 October 20-5 by selecting the appropriate phrase.

Hal's share of the profits and losses in the partnership has

INCREASED / DECREASED / STAYED THE SAME

after the change in the partnership agreement.

Hal's capital account balance has

INCREASED / DECREASED / STAYED THE SAME

after the change in the partnership agreement.

(c) Identify whether the following statements are true or false by putting a tick in the relevant column of the table below.

✔

Statement	True	False
When a new partner is admitted to a partnership business, existing partners pay a premium to welcome the new partner		
When a partner retires from a partnership business, the balance of his or her capital and current accounts is paid to the partner from the partnership bank account (subject to sufficient funds being available)		

You have the following information about a partnership business:

- The financial year ends on 31 March.
- The partners are Amy, Bob and Caz.
- Interest on capital is allowed at 5.0% per annum on the capital account balances at the end of the financial year.
- Interest on drawings is charged to the partners and is shown in the table below.

	Amy	Bob	Caz
	£	£	£
Annual salaries	10,000	12,500	nil
Capital account balances, 31 March 20-5	60,000	35,000	26,000
Capital account balances, 31 March 20-6	65,000	35,000	28,000
Drawings for the year	30,000	28,500	8,500
Interest on drawings for the year	300	285	85

- The profit for distribution to the partners after appropriations is £43,000.
- Profits are shared in the following percentages: Amy 50%, Bob 30%, Caz 20%.

(d) Prepare the current accounts for the partners for the year ended 31 March 20-6. Show clearly the balances carried down.

- You MUST enter zeros where appropriate.
- Do NOT use brackets, minus signs or dashes.

Select your entries from the following list:

Balance b/d, Balance c/d, Bank, Capital – Amy, Capital – Bob, Capital – Caz, Current – Amy, Current – Bob, Current – Caz, Drawings, Goodwill, Interest on capital, Interest on drawings, Salaries, Share of loss, Share of profit.

Current accounts

	Amy £	Bob £	Caz £		Amy £	Bob £	Caz £
Balance b/d			210	Balance b/d	2,320	830	

Task 5

This task is about preparing a partnership statement of financial position.

You are preparing the statement of financial position for the Blenheim partnership as at 31 March 20-6.

The partners are Yan and Zeb.

You have the final trial balance on the opposite page. All the necessary year end adjustments have been made, except for the transfer of £36,000 profit to the current accounts of the partners. Partners share profits and losses in the ratio 2:3, with Zeb taking the larger share.

(a) Calculate the balance of each partner's current account after sharing profits. Indicate whether these balances are DEBIT or CREDIT.

Current account: Yan £	DEBIT / CREDIT
Current account: Zeb £	DEBIT / CREDIT

(b) Prepare a statement of financial position for the partnership as at 31 March 20-6. You need to use the partners' current account balances that you have just calculated in (a).

Do NOT use brackets, minus signs or dashes.

Blenheim Partnership
Trial balance as at 31 March 20-6

	Dr £	Cr £
Accruals		550
Administration expenses	39,179	
Bank	11,355	
Capital account – Yan		35,000
Capital account – Zeb		50,000
Closing inventory	17,830	17,830
Current account – Yan	820	
Current account – Zeb		2,090
Depreciation charges	5,400	
Discounts received		1,210
Disposal of non-current asset	455	
Irrecoverable debts	394	
Machinery at cost	87,500	
Machinery accumulated depreciation		22,840
Opening inventory	16,380	
Payroll expenses	33,865	
Payroll liabilities		240
Prepayments	725	
Purchases	261,340	
Purchases ledger control		33,025
Sales		390,860
Sales returns	2,390	
Sales ledger control	64,055	
Travel expenses	14,497	
Value Added Tax		2,540
Total	556,185	556,185

Select your entries from the following list:

Accruals, Bank, Capital accounts, Current accounts, Expenses, Inventory, Machinery, Payroll liabilities, Prepayments, Purchases, Purchases returns, Sales, Sales returns, Trade payables, Trade receivables, Value Added Tax.

Blenheim Partnership
Statement of financial position as at 31 March 20-6

	£	£	£
Non-current assets	Cost	Accumulated depreciation	Carrying amount
Current assets			
Total current assets			
Current liabilities			
Total current liabilities			
Net current assets			
Net assets			
Financed by:	Yan	Zeb	Total

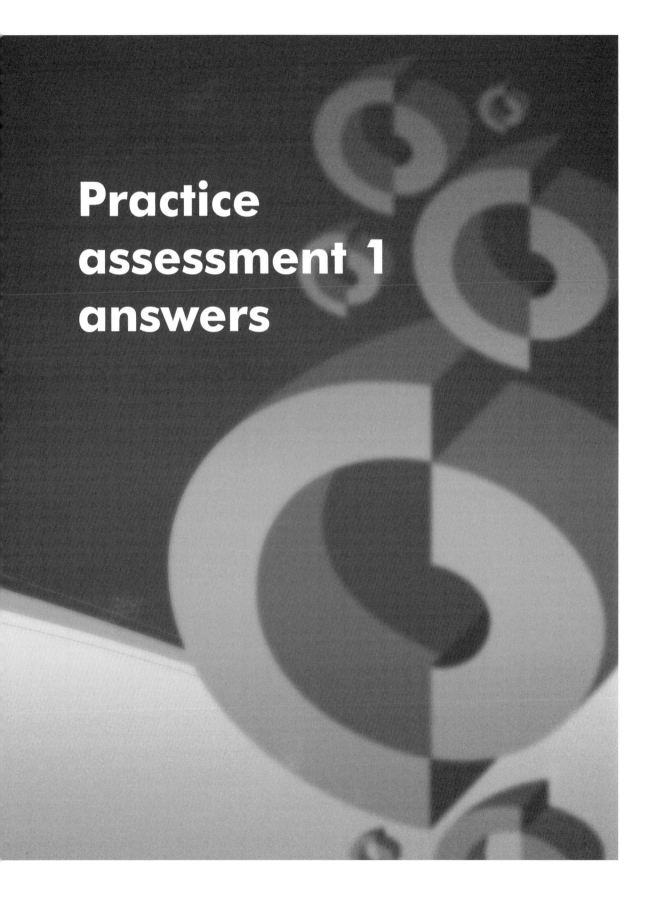

Practice
assessment 1
answers

Task 1

(a)

Sales ledger control account

Balance b/d	18,275	Sales returns day book	2,880
Sales day book	160,800	Bank	152,490
		Discounts allowed	230
		Balance c/d	23,475
	179,075		179,075

(b)

Purchases ledger control account

Purchases returns day book	1,920	Balance b/d	10,365
Bank	92,845	Purchases day book	98,400
Discounts received	550		
Balance c/d	13,450		
	108,765		108,765

(c)

VAT control account

Sales returns day book	480	Balance b/d	2,140
Purchases day book	16,400	Sales day book	26,800
Office expenses	4,120	Purchases returns day book	320
Bank	5,245		
Balance c/d	3,015		
	29,260		29,260

Task 2

(a)   Assets: £49,220

Liabilities: £21,890

Capital: £27,330

(b)   £52,090

Workings: £51,420 – £7,240 + £6,180 + £1,730

(c)   An intangible non-current asset which does not have material substance

(d)

Source of information	Missing figures				
	Total sales	Total purchases	Closing inventory	Profit for year	Non-current assets
Bank statement	✔				
Physical inventory count			✔		
Gross sales margin		✔			

Task 3

(a)   £159,930   ie £160,830 – £900

(b)

Tairo Trading Statement of profit or loss for the year ended 31 March 20-1		
	£	£
Sales revenue		159,930
Opening inventory	6,290	
Purchases	93,760	
Closing inventory	–8,350	
Cost of sales		91,700
Gross profit		68,230
Add:		
Allowance for doubtful debts adjustment		100
Less:		
Depreciation charges	6,240	
Discounts allowed	350	
General expenses	13,860	
Payroll expenses	28,450	
Rent and rates	10,390	
Total expenses		59,290
Profit/loss for the year		9,040

(c)   As a current asset

(d)   Drawings are deducted from capital in the statement of financial position

Task 4

(a)   **Capital account – Kay**

	£		£
Loan	25,000	Balance b/d	48,500
Bank	35,500	Goodwill	12,000
	60,500		60,500

(b)

Statement	True	False
All partnership agreements state that profits and losses must be shared equally between the partners		✔
A partnership agreement will state the salaries to be paid to employees		✔
A partnership agreement may state that interest is to be allowed on partners' capitals, and at what rate	✔	
A partnership agreement may state that interest is to be charged on partners' drawings, and at what rate	✔	

Task 4(c)

Partnership appropriation account for the year ended 31 March 20-1

	1 April 20-0 – 30 June 20-0 £	1 July 20-0 – 31 March 20-1 £	Total £
Profit for appropriation	17,000	51,000	68,000
Salaries:			
Jane	5,000	15,000	20,000
Kate	6,000	18,000	24,000
Lysa	0	0	0
Interest on capital:			
Jane	300	900	1,200
Kate	450	1,350	1,800
Lysa	0	300	300
Profit available for distribution	5,250	15,450	20,700

Profit share			
Jane	3,150	7,725	10,875
Kate	2,100	4,635	6,735
Lysa	0	3,090	3,090
Total profit distributed	5,250	15,450	20,700

Task 5

(a) Current account: Yulia £4,300 CREDIT

Current account: Zoe £5,700 CREDIT

(b) **Beacon Partnership**
Statement of financial position as at 31 March 20-1

	£	£	£
Non-current assets	Cost	Accumulated depreciation	Carrying amount
Office equipment	24,400	10,250	14,150
Current assets			
Inventory		17,380	
Trade receivables		*33,980	
Bank		11,750	
Cash		220	
Total current assets		63,330	
Current liabilities			
Trade payables	11,680		
Value Added Tax	3,110		
Accruals	690		
Total current liabilities		15,480	
Net current assets			47,850
Net assets			62,000
Financed by:	Yulia	Zoe	Total
Capital accounts	30,000	22,000	52,000
Current accounts	4,300	5,700	10,000
	34,300	27,700	62,000

* sales ledger control £35,380 minus allowance for doubtful debts £1,400

Note: bank £11,750 + cash £220 = cash and cash equivalents £11,970

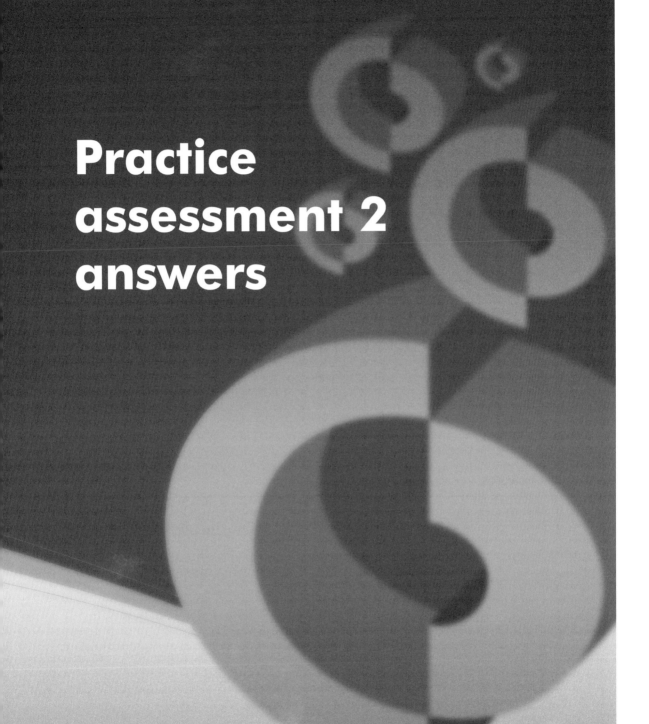

Practice
assessment 2
answers

Task 1

(a)

Purchases ledger control account

Discounts received	305	Balance b/d	12,600
Bank	102,145	Purchases day book	103,200
Balance c/d	13,350		
	115,800		115,800

(b)

VAT control account

Purchases day book	17,200	Balance b/d	3,290
Administration expenses	4,060	Sales day book	30,800
Bank	8,680		
Balance c/d	4,150		
	34,090		34,090

(c)

Bank account

Sales ledger control	183,110	Balance b/d	2,430
		Purchases ledger control	102,145
		HMRC for VAT	8,680
		Administration expenses	24,360
		Payroll expenses	25,490
		Drawings	16,300
		Balance c/d	3,705
	183,110		183,110

Task 2

(a)   £38,450

(b)

	Non-current assets	Current assets	Current liabilities	Non-current liabilities
Office equipment	✔			
Inventory		✔		
Bank loan				✔
Trade receivables		✔		
Goodwill	✔			

(c)   £307,000

Workings:

Gross profit = £400,000 x 25% =   £100,000

Cost of sales = £400,000 – £100,000 = £300,000

Purchases = opening inventory   £38,000

             + purchases   ?

             – closing inventory   £45,000

             = cost of sales   £300,000

             therefore purchases =   £307,000

(d)

Source of information	Missing figures			
	Bank statement	Physical inventory count	Trade receivables	Gross sales margin
Closing inventory		✔		
Cash sales	✔			
Total purchases				✔

Task 3

(a)   £140,730

(b)

Dracus Trading Statement of profit or loss for the year ended 31 March 20-1		
	£	£
Sales revenue		240,340
Opening inventory	17,420	
Purchases	140,730	
Closing inventory	−18,190	
Cost of sales		139,960
Gross profit		100,380
Add:		
Discounts received		230
Less:		
Depreciation charges	7,240	
Payroll expenses	56,890	
Rent and rates	16,780	
Total expenses		80,910
Profit/loss for the year		19,700

(c)   As a current liability

(d)   A bank loan repayable in two years' time

(e)

Statement	True	False
A trial balance which balances proves that no errors have been made in the double-entry		✔
A trial balance gives a profit figure		✔
The closing inventory is recognised in both columns of the trial balance, except when it is included in a cost of sales account	✔	
A trial balance distinguishes between the figures that relate to the statement of profit or loss and the figures that relate to the statement of financial position		✔

Task 4

(a)

Partners' capital accounts

	Freya	Gina		Freya	Gina
	£	£		£	£
Goodwill	12,000	18,000	Balances b/d	24,000	36,000
Balances c/d	27,000	33,000	Goodwill	15,000	15,000
	39,000	51,000		39,000	51,000

(b)

Transaction	Capital account		Current account	
	Dr	Cr	Dr	Cr
Capital introduced		✔		
Partner's salary				✔
Drawings			✔	
Goodwill created		✔		
Share of profits				✔
Interest on capital				✔

(c)

Current accounts

	Rob £	Sue £	Tom £		Rob £	Sue £	Tom £
Balance b/d	0	0	250	Balance b/d	650	1,200	0
Drawings	16,200	25,900	14,600	Salaries	10,840	13,690	10,900
Interest on drawings	250	325	300	Interest on capital	1,000	1,400	600
Balances c/d	1,540	3,265	0	Share of profit	5,500	13,200	3,300
				Balance c/d	0	0	350
	17,990	29,490	15,150		17,990	29,490	15,150

Task 5

(a)   Current account: Sara £4,120   CREDIT

       Current account: Toni   £3,360   CREDIT

(b)   **Sarton Partnership**
       Statement of financial position as at 31 March 20-6

	£	£	£
Non-current assets	**Cost**	**Accumulated depreciation**	**Carrying amount**
Vehicles	29,500	12,800	16,700
Current assets			
Inventory		6,090	
Trade receivables		*9,530	
Prepayments		440	
Bank		10,330	
Total current assets		26,390	
Current liabilities			
Trade payables	6,420		
Value Added Tax	1,290		
Accruals	400		
Total current liabilities		8,110	
Net current assets			18,280
Net assets			34,980
Financed by:	**Sara**	**Toni**	**Total**
Capital accounts	15,000	12,500	27,500
Current accounts	4,120	3,360	7,480
	19,120	15,860	34,980

* sales ledger control £10,360 minus allowance for doubtful debts £830.

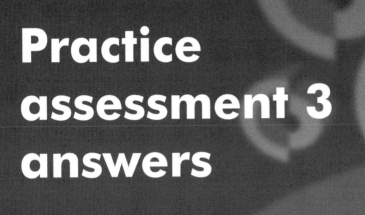

Practice assessment 3 answers

Task 1

(a)

Purchases ledger control account

	£		£
Bank	27,846	Balance b/d	4,367
Balance c/d	4,498	Credit purchases	27,977
	32,344		32,344

(b)

Sales ledger control account

Balance b/d	8,216	Bank	67,031
Credit sales	68,422	Irrecoverable debts	560
		Balance c/d	9,047
	76,638		76,638

(c)

Bank account

Sales ledger control	67,031	Balance b/d	3,219
		Purchases ledger control	27,846
		Drawings	12,500
		Office expenses	19,361
		Bank interest paid	247
		Cash purchases	2,612
		Balance c/d	1,246
	67,031		67,031

Task 2

(a)

Capital account

	£		£
Balance c/d	21,200	Balance b/d	0
		Bank	20,000
		Purchases	1,200
	21,200		21,200

(b)

	Increase	Decrease	No change
Assets			✔
Liabilities			✔
Capital			✔

(c)   £64,000 [calculation: (£80,000 ÷ 125) x 100]

(d)   £3,340 [calculation: £67,340 – £64,000]

(e)   Cheques to suppliers sent out at the end of the month have not yet cleared

Task 3

(a) £123,700 ie £125,860 – £2,160

(b) £49,290 ie £47,860 + £1,430

(c)

Hanslo Trading Statement of profit or loss for the year ended 31 March 20-6		
	£	£
Sales revenue		123,700
Opening inventory	9,760	
Purchases	49,290	
Closing inventory	−11,340	
Cost of sales		47,710
Gross profit		75,990
Add:		
Disposal of non-current assets		990
Less:		
Carriage outwards	2,790	
Depreciation charges	4,520	
General expenses	23,920	
Payroll expenses	49,050	
Total expenses		80,280
Profit/loss for the year		−3,300

(d) The business has made a loss on disposal

Task 4

(a)

Account name	Amount £	Debit	Credit
Goodwill	60,000		✔
Capital – Hal	36,000	✔	
Capital – Ian	24,000	✔	

(b) Hal's share of the profits and losses in the partnership has DECREASED after the change in the partnership agreement.

Hal's capital account balance has INCREASED after the change in the partnership agreement.

(c)

Statement	True	False
When a new partner is admitted to a partnership business, existing partners pay a premium to welcome the new partner		✔
When a partner retires from a partnership business, the balance of his or her capital and current accounts is paid to the partner from the partnership bank account (subject to sufficient funds being available)	✔	

(d)

Current accounts

	Amy £	Bob £	Caz £		Amy £	Bob £	Caz £
Balance b/d			210	Balance b/d	2,320	830	
Drawings	30,000	28,500	8,500	Salaries	10,000	12,500	0
Interest on drawings	300	285	85	Interest on capital	3,250	1,750	1,400
Balance c/d	6,770		1,205	Share of profit	21,500	12,900	8,600
				Balance c/d		805	
	37,070	28,785	10,000		37,070	28,785	10,000

Task 5

(a) Current account: Yan £13,580 CREDIT

Current account: Zeb £23,690 CREDIT

(b) **Blenheim Partnership**
Statement of financial position as at 31 March 20-6

	£	£	£
Non-current assets	Cost	Accumulated depreciation	Carrying amount
Machinery	87,500	22,840	64,660
Current assets			
Inventory		17,830	
Trade receivables		64,055	
Prepayments		725	
Bank		11,355	
Total current assets		93,965	
Current liabilities			
Trade payables	33,025		
Value Added Tax	2,540		
Accruals	550		
Payroll liabilities	240		
Total current liabilities		36,355	
Net current assets			57,610
Net assets			122,270
Financed by:	Yan	Zeb	Total
Capital accounts	35,000	50,000	85,000
Current accounts	13,580	23,690	37,270
	48,580	73,690	122,270

for your notes

for your notes

for your notes

for your notes